big
NATE
THUNKA, THUNKA, THUNKA

More

big NATE

adventures from

LINCOLN PEIRCE

big NATE

THUNKA, THUNKA, THUNKA

by LINCOLN PEIRCE

SCHOLASTIC INC.

7

MY DAD IS A TOTAL HYPOCRITE.

HOW SO?

HE MAKES SUCH A BIG DEAL ABOUT HANDING OUT HEALTHY TREATS FOR HALLOWEEN!

BUT WHY DOES THAT MAKE HIM A HYPOCRITE?

IT DOESN'T. STEALING CANDY FROM MY STASH DOES.

STEP AWAY FROM THE PUMPKIN, DAD!

WHA-? WHO, ME?

Peirce

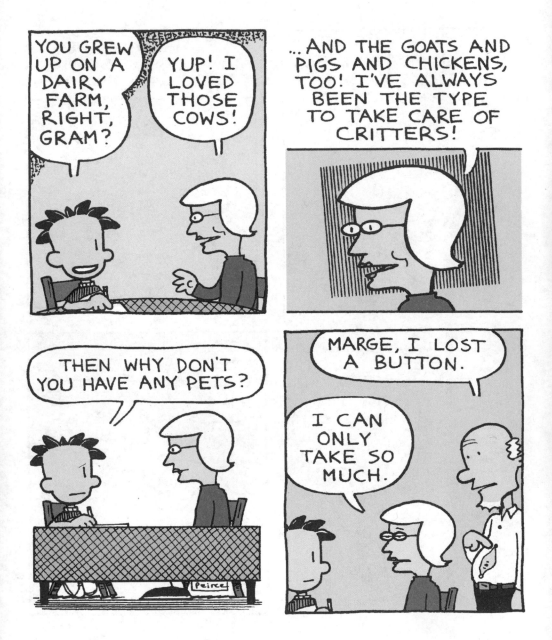

23

HEY, **I'VE** GOT AN IDEA! NEXT TIME MARCUS INSULTS YOU, JUST **YO MAMA** HIM!

YOU CAN'T "JUST YO MAMA" PEOPLE, FRANCIS!

YOU ONLY DO IT DURING A "YO MAMA SMACKDOWN"! YOU DON'T YO MAMA PEOPLE AT **RANDOM!**

HOW WOULD YOU FEEL IF, OUT OF NOWHERE, I SAID TO YOU: "YO MAMA'S SO FAT, HER THIGHS ARE WHERE CORDUROY GOES TO DIE"?

UM... BAD.

EXACTLY! SEE, I'D NEVER **DO** THAT!

WHY DO YOU HAVE TO WAIT FOR MARCUS TO INSULT **YOU** BEFORE YOU INSULT **HIM**? WHY DON'T YOU GO **FIRST**?

FRANCIS, IF I JUST WALK UP TO MARCUS AND INSULT HIM, HE'LL **CLOCK** ME!

...BUT IF I COME UP WITH A WELL-TIMED, WITTY COMEBACK, **I'LL** BE THE GUY WHO PUT THE BULLY IN HIS **PLACE**! I'LL BE A **HERO**!

I'LL GET A STANDING OVATION... GIRLS WILL ADORE ME... THE YEAR-BOOK WILL PR... AGE A... MY IM... WAY

SOMEONE'S BEEN WATCHING TOO MANY TV MOVIES.

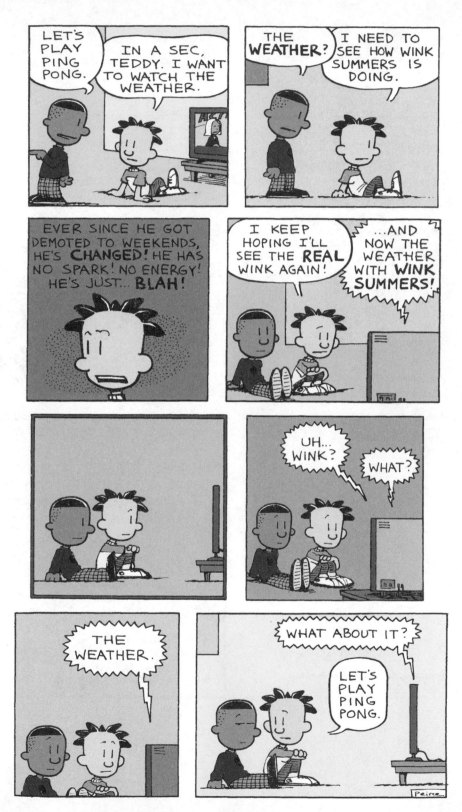

41

45

47

Panel 1:
YOUR SISTER GAVE ME HER CHRISTMAS WISH LIST. THERE ARE ONLY TWO ITEMS ON HERE YOU CAN AFFORD.

YEAH? WHAT?

Panel 2:
YOU COULD BUY HER THE NEW "BETHANY" TREASURY...

"BETHANY"? THE WORLD'S LAMEST COMIC STRIP?

Panel 3:
NO **WAY!** I REFUSE TO SPEND MY HARD-EARNED MONEY ON THE SO-CALLED "HEARTWARMING" ADVENTURES OF A TEENAGE **AIRHEAD!**

Panel 4:
...OR YOU COULD BUY HER SOME "ME SO SASSY" UNDERWEAR.

HELLO, BOOK-STORE.

Peirce

65

68

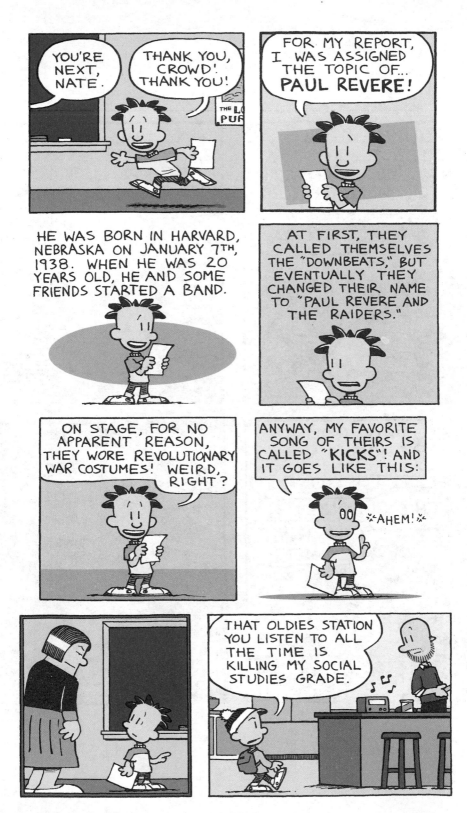

69

I'M NOT VERY GOOD AT DRAWING.

DAD, **RELAX!** IT'S JUST A **GAME!**

THE SCRIBBLE GAME ISN'T ABOUT MAKING PERFECT DRAWINGS! IT'S ABOUT HAVING **FUN!** YOU **CAN'T** DO IT WRONG!

YES, YOU CAN. IT'S A DUCK.

76

THE WEEK'S HALF OVER, GINA, AND NATE HASN'T GOT A SINGLE DETENTION!

THERE'S STILL PLENTY OF TIME.

YEAH, BUT HE'S GOT ALL THE TEACHERS EATING OUT OF THE PALM OF HIS HAND!

OH, **PLEASE**! THE TEACHERS **HATE** HIM!

DON'T BE LITTERB[U]
KEEP OUR CLEAN

THE IDEA THAT HE COULD SUDDENLY BECOME THEIR **FAVORITE** IS A TOTAL **JOKE**!

...AND THEN THE CAMEL SAYS: "DUCK? **WHAT** DUCK?"

HA HA HA HA! VERY FUNNY, SIR!

!!

Peirce

89

93

YOU'RE FAMILIAR WITH THE SCHOOL HANDBOOK, GINA, SO YOU SHOULD KNOW THAT BETTING IS PROHIBITED AT P.S. 38.

I'M DISAPPOINTED IN YOU.

BUT... IT WASN'T JUST **ME**! AREN'T YOU DISAPPOINTED IN **NATE**, TOO?

NO... WITH NATE, IT'S NOT DISAPPOINTMENT.

IT'S MORE LIKE NUMB ACCEPTANCE.

HA! TAKE **THAT**, GINA!

I'M STUDYING A BUNCH OF FAMOUS FIGHT SONGS TO GET SOME IDEAS FOR MY OWN!

HERE'S A CLASSIC! "CHEER, CHEER FOR OLD NOTRE DAME. WAKE UP THE ECHOES CHEERING HER NAME. SEND A VOLLEY CHEER ON HIGH, SHAKE DOWN THE THUNDER FROM THE SKY."

"WAKE UP THE ECHOES." THAT'S COOL.

YEAH. EXCEPT IT DOESN'T REALLY MAKE SENSE FOR P.S. 38.

THE ONLY ECHOES AROUND HERE ARE IN THE THIRD-FLOOR BATHROOM.

MIGHT BE TOUGH TO WORK THAT INTO A SONG LYRIC.

119

CLASS, YOUR SIXTH GRADE BOOK BUDDIES ARE HERE!

HI, MRS. BIGBEE!

HELLO, NATE.

HEY, WHERE'S MY BOOK BUDDY?

I'M AFRAID PETER'S ABSENT TODAY... BUT THERE'S **ANOTHER** CHILD WHO NEEDS A BUDDY.

MIRANDA? WILL YOU COME HERE, PLEASE?

NO!

SHE MAY HAVE HAD A BIT TOO MUCH SUGAR AT SNACK TIME.

NATE, TAKE YOUR SEAT AND PAY ATTENTION TO MR. CAVENDISH.

I DON'T **WANT** TO PAY ATTENTION TO HIM!

I WANT TO HEAR ABOUT THE WEATHER FROM **WINK SUMMERS!** BUT THE GENIUSES AT CHANNEL 12 CANNED WINK AND BROUGHT IN **THIS** GUY!

THEY DIDN'T CARE ABOUT WINK! THEY ONLY CARED ABOUT GIVING THEIR VIEWERS SOME **EYE CANDY!**

HE BROUGHT **CANDY?**

IT'S AN EXPRESSION, CHAD. RELAX.

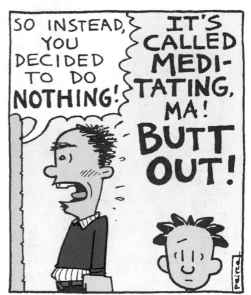

140

143

148

footer:

151

WAIT A MINUTE, KIM! HOW COME YOU'RE PLAYING BASEBALL? GIRLS PLAY **SOFTBALL!**

THERE **IS** NO SOFTBALL.

NOT ENOUGH GIRLS SIGNED UP, SO THE LEAGUE DISBANDED AND I SWITCHED TO BASEBALL.

SO NOW WE'RE TEAMMATES.

YEAH, THAT'S... THAT'S...

INCREDIBLY ROMANTIC.

NO!

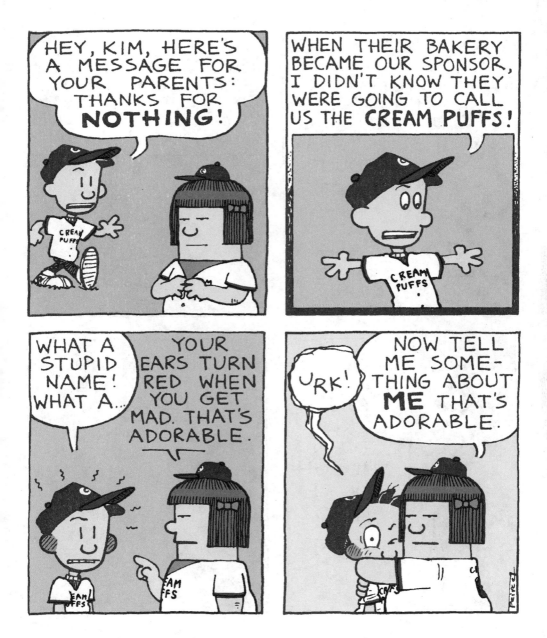

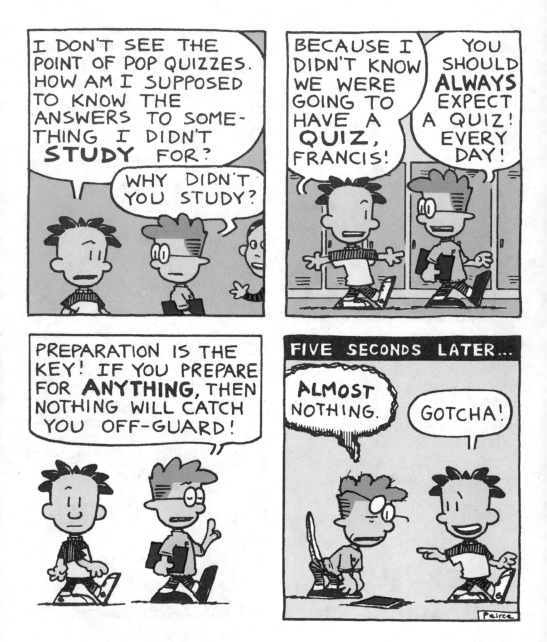

NATE, YOUR PERFORMANCE ON YESTERDAY'S QUIZ WAS, TO BE CHARITABLE, **DISMAL.**

FOR EXAMPLE, QUESTION NUMBER THREE ASKED: WHO WAS THOMAS PAINE?

THE CORRECT RESPONSE WOULD HAVE BEEN THAT HE WAS ONE OF THE FOUNDING FATHERS AND THE AUTHOR OF "COMMON SENSE."...

...**NOT** A "GRAMMY-WINNING RAPPER WHO IS CHANGING THE FACE OF HIP-HOP"!

SO THEY'RE BOTH REVOLUTIONARIES.

ISBN 978-1-338-11827-8

12 11 10 9 8 7 6 5 4 3 2   16 17 18 19 20 21

Printed in the U.S.A.   40

First Scholastic printing, November 2016

These strips appeared in newspapers from
October 31, 2011, through April 21, 2012.